for Alison, John and Bridget

First published in 1994 by
Cornerhouse Publications
70 Oxford Street
Manchester M1 5NH
England
Tel 0161 237 9662
Fax 0161 237 9664

Photographs and Text © Bill Hirst
Introductory Text © Benoit Mandelbrot

Hardback ISBN 0 948797 24 X
Softback ISBN 0 948797 23 1

A CIP catalogue record for this book is available from the British Library

Design: Bill Hirst
Production Co-ordination: Niall Allsop
Prints: Bill Hirst
Reprographics: Leeds Photo Litho
Print: Jackson Wilson

Fractal Landscapes
from the Real World

Cornerhouse Publications

Above The Burren, Co. Clare, Eire *Endpapers* slate waste, Tanygrisiau, North Wales

Fractal Landscapes

from the Real World

photographs by **Bill Hirst** with an introduction by **Benoit Mandelbrot**

FRACTALS AS A MORPHOLOGY OF THE AMORPHOUS

Benoit B Mandelbrot

Yale University

New Haven CT 06520

USA

To complement his magnificent photographs, Bill Hirst has invited me to say a few words about fractal geometry. This term means many different things to many different people. But one of its meanings can be viewed as standing above the others: fractal geometry is a recent mathematical and graphic implementation of some very old and basic insights of our culture, and perhaps even of all cultures of mankind. Let us start with a problem that is implicitly set up in the *Bible*. In the King James Version, the first lines of *Genesis* inform us that:

> "In the beginning God created the heaven and the earth.
>
> And the earth was without form ...
>
> And God said, Let there be light: and there was light ...
>
> And God made the firmament ... and it was so ...
>
> And God said, Let ... the dry land appear: and it was so."

The existence of light eventually begat optics; the existence of a firmament begat astronomy; the existence of land begat geology, and other sciences arose in the same vein from many of the later lines of *Genesis*.

Yet, most aspects of the heaven and the earth were never made orderly. They remained without form: *tohu va vohu* in the original Hebrew.

The over-reaching goal of my scientific life can now be stated: I have spent it looking for elements of order in *tohu va vohu*. In due time, those elements became organised in a discipline I called *fractal geometry*.

From the sublime to the merely remarkable, consider these words by the painter Eugene Delacroix (1798-1853) writing in the *Revue Britannique* in 1850.

> "Swedenborg claims, in his theory of nature, ... that the lungs are composed of a number of little lungs, the liver of little livers, the spleen of little spleens, etc."

> "Without being such a grand observer, I have noticed this truth for a long time. I have often said that the branches of a tree are themselves little trees; fragments of rocks are similar to masses of rocks, particles of earth to enormous piles of

earth. I am persuaded that one would find a quantity of such analogies. A feather is composed of a million feathers."

Incidentally, Swedenborg was also cited by Emerson.

Let us continue with a few words by Edward Whymper (1840-1910), the first explorer to climb the Matterhorn and author of *Scrambles Amongst the Alps in 1860-1869.*

> "It is worthy of remark that ... fragments of ... rock ... often present the characteristic forms of cliffs from which they have been broken ... Why should it not be so if the mountain's mass is more or less homogeneous? The same causes which produce the small forms fashion the large ones; the same influences are at work – the same frost and rain give shape to the mass as well as to its parts."

These quotes by Delacroix and Whymper introduce a second basic theme, that of self-similarity.

Fractal geometry is a branch of learning, more precisely, of knowing and feeling, that I conceived and built around the above two inter-twined threads of thought: disorder in nature and self-similarity.

In its fully formalised form, fractal geometry is an enterprise in mathematics whose primary purpose is to help physics, geophysics and other sciences. But in the process of reaching this goal, fractal geometry has the very distinctive feature of putting enormous reliance upon the eye.

Human babies – contrary to kittens – are born with open eyes, but they must learn to see. Much of learning comes from experience and requires no theory. But in many cases, theory can be of great help, or at least of great influence, witness the following words by Paul Cézanne (1839-1906) in a letter to E. Bernard, April 15, 1904.

> "Treat nature according to the cylinder, the sphere and the cone, with everything put in proper perspective, so that each side of an object or a plane is directed toward a central point"

It happens that I admire most paintings by Cézanne, but not the preceding statement. More specifically, I endorse unhesitatingly its general thrust, that one cannot see without a theory, hence different theories lead to different forms of art. But my disagreement was stated forcibly in the following lines, which open my book, *The Fractal Geometry of Nature.*

> "Why is geometry often described as "cold" and "dry?" One reason lies in its inability to describe the shape of a cloud, a mountain, a coastline, or a tree. Clouds are not spheres, mountains are not cones, coastlines are not circles, and bark is not smooth, nor does lightning travel in a straight line."

> "More generally, I claim that many patterns of Nature are so irregular and fragmented, that, compared with Euclid (an old English term I use to denote all of standard geometry) Nature exhibits not simply a higher degree but an altogether

different level of complexity. The number of distinct scales of length of natural patterns is for all practical purposes infinite." "The existence of these patterns challenges us to study those forms that Euclid leaves aside as being "formless," to investigate the morphology of the "amorphous.""..."

"Responding to this challenge, I conceived and developed a new geometry of nature and implemented its use in a number of diverse fields. It describes many of the irregular and fragmented patterns around us, and leads to full-fledged theories, by identifying a family of shapes I call *fractals*."

My own experience, confirmed by many stories that I heard, suggests that acquaintance with fractals makes humans see the world differently. This can happen at several different levels. When a recent physics award cited me for having "changed our view of nature," it referred to the view of nature as expressed in physicists' writings. But Bill Hirst, himself a physicist, shows that this is not all. His magnificent photographs demonstrate that fractals not only changed his view of nature in an allegorical sense, but also changed it in the most literal sense one could imagine.

As we shall see in a moment, fractal geometry also has, in addition to its realistic face, a face that is thoroughly non-representational. Fractals are a family of geometric shapes, and I happen to believe that, in order to understand geometric shapes, one must see them. It has very

often been forgotten that geometry simply *must* have a visual component, and I believe that in many contexts this omission proved to be very harmful.

Fractal geometry is conveniently viewed as a language, and it has proven its value by its uses. Its uses in art and pure mathematics, being without "practical" application, can be said to be poetic. Its uses in various areas of the study of materials and of other areas of engineering are examples of practical prose. Its uses in physical theory, especially in conjunction with the basic equations of mathematical physics, combine poetry and high prose.

Let me remind you of a marvellous text that Galileo Galilei wrote at the dawn of science, in his book, *Il Saggiatore*, (1623):

"Philosophy is written in this great book – I am speaking of the Universe – which is constantly offered for our contemplation, but which cannot be read until we have learned its language and have become familiar with the characters in which it is written. It is written in the language of mathematics, and its characters are triangles, circles and other geometric forms, without which it is humanly impossible to understand a single word of it; without which one wanders in vain across a dark labyrinth."

We all know that mechanics and calculus, therefore all of quantitative science, were built on these characters, and we all know that these

Figure 1 A fractal landscape that never was
(R. F. Voss)

Figure 2 A cloud formation that never was
(S. Lovejoy & B. B. Mandelbrot)

characters belong to Euclidean geometry. In addition, we all agree with Galileo that this geometry is necessary to describe the world around us, beginning with the motion of planets and the fall of stones on Earth.

But is it sufficient? Figure 1 seems to represent a real mountain, but it is neither a photograph, nor a painting. It is a mathematical forgery, a computer forgery; it is completely based upon a mathematical formula from fractal geometry. The same is true of the forgery of a cloud shown in Figure 2.

An amusing and important feature of Figures 1 and 2 is that both are adaptations of formulae that had been known in pure mathematics. Thanks to fractal geometry, diverse mathematical objects, which used to be viewed as being very far from physics, indeed as being pathological, have turned out to be the proper tools for studying nature.

One of the successes of fractal modelling was unexpected and amusing. A fractal generator is used in an immortal masterpiece of cinematography called *Star Trek Two, the Wrath of Khan*. Many people have seen this film, but very few have noticed that the new planet that appears in the *Genesis* sequence of that film is fractal. If prodded, you would note peculiar characteristics (superhighways and square fields) that are due to a shortcut taken by Lucasfilm to make it possible to compute these fractals quickly enough. But we need not dwell on flaws. Far more interesting is the fact that the films that include fractals create a bridge between two activities that are not expected to ever meet, mathematics and physics on the one hand, and popular art on the other.

More generally, an aspect of fractals that I found very surprising at the beginning, and that continues to be a source of marvel, is that people respond to fractals in a deep, emotional fashion. They either like them or dislike them, but either emotion is completely at variance with the boredom that most people feel towards classical geometry.

Let me stop here to state that I will never say anything bad about

Euclid's geometry. I love it and it has been an important part of my life as a child and as a student; in fact the main reason why I survived academically despite chaotic schooling was that I could always use geometric intuition to cover my lack of skill as a manipulator of formulae. But we all know by experience that almost everybody except professional geometers views Euclid as being cold and dry. Fractal shapes are exactly as geometric as those of Euclid, yet they evoke emotions which geometry is not expected or supposed to evoke.

Let us now move from the geometry of the World around us to the proper geometry of deterministic chaos: it happens to be the same as the proper geometry of mountains and clouds. The fact that we need only one new geometry is really quite marvellous, because several might have been needed, in addition to that of Euclid. But it is not so. Fractal geometry plays both roles. Not only is it the proper language to describe the shape of mountains and of clouds, but it is also the proper language for all the geometric aspects of chaos.

To give an example, Figure 3 is an enormously magnified fragment from the set to which my name has been attached. Here, a fragment of the Mandelbrot Set has been magnified in a ratio equal to Avogadro's number, which is 6×10^{23}. Why choose this particular number? Because it's a nice, very large number, and a huge magnification provided a good opportunity for testing the quadruple precision arithmetic on the IBM computers that were being introduced a few years ago. (They passed the test. It's very amusing to be able to justify plain fun and

pure science on the basis of down-to-earth considerations.) If the whole Mandelbrot Set had been drawn on the same scale, the end of it would be somewhere near the star Sirius.

The shape of the black "bug" near the centre is very nearly the same as that of the white centre of Figure 11, which will show the shape of the whole Mandelbrot Set. Finding nearly identical bugs all over the Set is a token of geometric orderliness. On the other hand, the surrounding pattern depends very much upon the point on which the zoom has focussed; its variability is a token of variety, and even chaos.

The shape shown in Figure 4 is a variant of the Mandelbrot Set that corresponds to a slightly different formula. This shape is reproduced here simply to comment on a totally amazing and extraordinarily satisfying aspect of fractal geometry. Fractals are perceived by many people as being beautiful. But these shapes were initially developed for the purpose of science, for the purpose of understanding how the world is put together both statically (in terms of mountains) and dynamically (in terms of chaos, strange attractors, etc.). In other words, the shapes shown in Figures 1 to 4 were not *intended* to be beautiful. This being beautiful unavoidably raises many questions. The most important question is simply, why? The fact must tell us something about our system of visual perception.

I wanted to start with Figures 1 to 4 because their structure is so rich ... but I went overboard. Their structure is in fact so rich that these

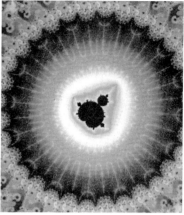

Figure 3 A very small fragment of the Mandelbrot Set (R. F. Voss)

Figure 4 A small fragment of a modified Mandelbrot Set (B. B. Mandelbrot)

Figure 5 Cauliflower Romanesco (R. Ishikawa)

figures cannot be used to explain the main feature of all fractals. The underlying basic principle shows far more clearly in Figure 5, which – for a change – reproduces a real photograph of a real object. You may recognise a variety of cauliflower called *Romanesco*. Each bud looks absolutely like the whole head, and in turn each bud sub-divides into smaller buds, and so on. I am told that the same structure repeats over the five levels of separation you can do by hand and see by the naked eye, and then over many more levels you can see only with a magnifying glass or microscope.

Until recently, scientists did not pay much attention to this "hierarchical" property. Their first reaction to this kind of botanical shape was not to focus on buds within buds, but on the spirals formed by the buds. This interest led to extensive knowledge about the relation between the golden mean (and the Fibonacci series), and the way plants spiral. But the hierarchical structure of buds is more important for us here, because it embodies the essential idea of a fractal.

Before we continue and tackle what a fractal is, let us ponder what a fractal *is not*. Take a geometric shape and examine it in increasing detail. That is, take smaller and smaller portions and enlarge each to some prescribed overall size. If our shape belongs to standard geometry, it is well known that the enlargements become increasingly smooth.

In sharp contrast, the shapes I have been showing *fail to be* locally linear. In fact, they deserve being called "geometrically chaotic," unless proven otherwise. In an altogether different neighbourhood of the great City of Science, a kind of geometric chaos became known during the half century from 1875 to 1925. Mathematicians, who were attempting to flee from concern with nature, became aware of the fact that a geometric shape's roughness need not vanish as the examination becomes more searching. It is conceivable that its roughness should either remain constant, or vary endlessly, up and down. The hold of standard geometry was so powerful, however, that the resulting shapes were not recognised as models of nature. Quite the contrary, they were labelled "monstrous" and "pathological." After discovering these sets, mathematics proceeded to increasingly greater generality.

Science must constantly navigate between two dangers: lack and excess of generality. Between the two extremes, it must always find the proper level that is necessary to do things right. Between the extremes of the excessive geometric order of Euclid, and of the true geometric chaos of the most general mathematics, can there be a middle ground of "organised" or "orderly" geometric chaos? To provide such a middle ground is the ambition of fractal geometry.

The reason why fractals are far more special than the most general shapes of mathematics is that they are characterised by transformations called "symmetries", which are invariances under dilations and/or contractions. Broadly speaking, mathematical and natural fractals are shapes whose roughness and fragmentation neither tend to vanish, nor fluctuate up and down, but remain *essentially unchanged* as one zooms in continually and examination is refined. Hence, the structure of every piece holds the key to the whole structure.

The preceding statement is made precise and illustrated by Figure 6, which represents a shape that is enormously simpler than Figures 1 to 5. As a joke, I called it the *Sierpinski gasket*, and the joke has stuck.

The four small diagrams show the point of departure of the construction, then its first three stages, while the large diagram shows an advanced stage. The basic step of the construction is to divide a given (black) triangle into four sub-triangles, and then erase (whiten) the middle fourth. This step is first performed with a wholly black filled-in triangle of side 1, then with three black triangles of side 1/2. This process continues, following a pattern called *recursive deletion*, which is very widely used to construct fractals.

By examining the large advanced stage picture, it is obvious that each of the three reduced gaskets is simply superposed on one third of the overall shape. For this reason, the fractal gasket is said to have the property of *exact* or *linear* self-similarity.

I used to think that the word "self-similarity" was used for the first time in a paper of mine in 1964. But it has since come to my attention that the philosopher Emerson had used it once before me in the context of the citation by Delacroix early in this text. Now, why was this word never used, although the idea itself is perfectly obvious and very old? The reason is that finding a shape to be self-similar had no importance

until my work. For example, Sierpinski had investigated "his" shape for a long forgotten purpose for which the only virtue of self-similarity was that it resulted in a shape requiring few lines to describe.

Why did self-similarity become important? Because Figures 1 to 5 are self-similar, not – to be sure – in an exact, but in a statistical meaning of the word. One reason why fractal geometry has developed so widely, and I spent so much time in efforts to build it as a discipline, resides in empirical discoveries (each established by a separate investigation) that the relief of the earth is self-similar, and that the same is true of many other shapes around us.

The Sierpinski gasket, and other structures of the same ilk, are important because you must begin the study of fractal geometry with them, but keep in mind that the real fun begins *beyond* them.

The fun begins after one has added an element of unpredictability, which may be due to either randomness (as in Figures 1, 2 and 5), or to non-linearity (as in Figures 3 and 4). Non-linearity is the key word of the new meaning of chaos, namely of deterministic chaos, and randomness is the key to chaos in the old sense of the word. The two are very intimately linked.

Figure 7, overleaf, combines a sequence of completely artificial random landscapes. Each part of this picture consists of enlarging a small black rectangle in the preceding picture, and in filling in additional detail. This procedure is called *recursive addition*. Each step followed by a

Figure 6 The Sierpinski gasket. Early and late stages of construction

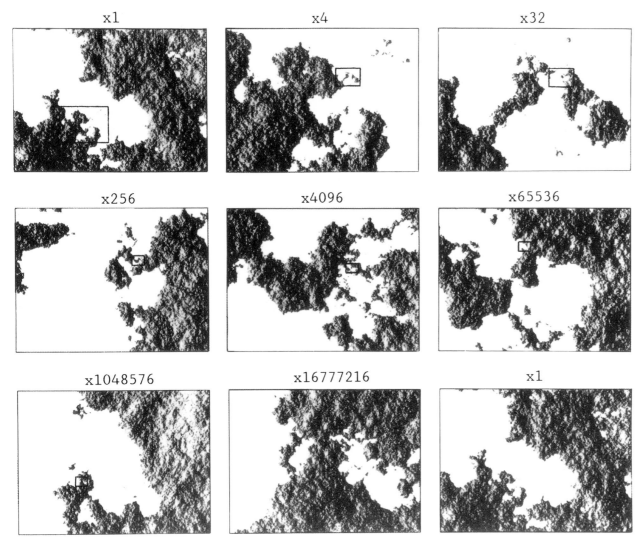

x1   x4   x32

x256   x4096   x65536

x1048576   x16777216   x1

Figure 7 Zoom onto a fractal landscape that never was (R. F. Voss)

"zooming-in" yields a landscape that is of course different from the preceding landscape. It is more detailed, yet at the same time is qualitatively the same. The successive enlargements might have been different parts of the same coastline examined on the same scale, but in fact they are

neighbourhoods of one single point examined at very different scales. Clearly, these successive enlargements of a coastline completely fail to become locally smooth!

At this point, let me recall a story about the great difficulties the ancient Greeks used to experience in defining "size." Much evidence suggested Sardinia was smaller than Sicily, but sailors claimed that Sardinia was the larger of the two because it took longer to circumnavigate; because its coastline was longer. But let us examine Figure 8, and ponder the notion of the length of a coastline? When the ship used to circumnavigate is large, the captain will report a rather small length. A much smaller ship would come closer to the shore, and navigate along a longer curve. A man walking along the coastline will measure an even longer length. So what about the "real length of the coast of Sardinia?" The question seems both elementary and silly, but it turns out to have an unexpected answer. The answer is, "It depends." The length of a coastline depends on whether you circumnavigate in a large or a small ship, or walk along it, or use dividers or some other instrument to measure the coastline on a map.

The preceding example makes us appreciate the extraordinary power of the mental structure that schools have imposed by teaching Euclid. Many people who thought they had never understood geometry have learned enough to expect every curve to have a length. For the curves in which I am interested, this turns out to have been the wrong thing to remember from school, because the theoretical length is infinite, and the practical length depends on the method of measurement. Its increase is faster where the coastline is rough, making it necessary to study the notion of roughness.

The task of measuring roughness objectively has turned out to be extraordinarily difficult. People whose work demands it, like metallurgists, seem to ask their friends in statistics for a number one could measure and call roughness. But perform the following experiment. Take different samples of steel which the US National Bureau of Standards guarantees to be pieces of one block of metal, as homogenous as man can make it. If you take several pieces and you break them all and measure the roughness of the fractures according to the books on statistics, you will get values that are in complete disagreement.

On the other hand, I shall argue that roughness happens to be measured consistently by a quantity called *fractal dimension*, which happens in general to be a fraction, and which one can measure very accurately. Studying many samples from the same block of metal, we found the same dimension for every sample.

The reason for the term "dimension" is that the same approach can also be applied to points, intervals, full squares and full cubes, and in those cases yields the familiar values 0, 1, 2 and 3. Applied to fractals, however, measurements usually yield values that are not integers.

Fractal geometry has proved an increasingly valuable tool in the discovery and study of new aspects of nature. *Diffusion Limited Aggregates*, DLA, are a form of random growth. A DLA cluster lurks in the centre of Figure 9. It is a tree-like shape of baffling complexity one can use to model how ash forms, how water seeps through rock, how cracks spread in a solid and how lightning discharges.

To see how the growth proceeds, take a very large chess board and put a queen, which is not allowed to move, in the central square. Pawns, which are allowed to move in either of the four directions on the board, are released from a random starting point at the edge of the board, and are instructed to perform a random walk, or drunkard's walk. The direction of each step is chosen from four equal probabilities. When a pawn reaches a square next to that of the original queen, it transforms itself into a new queen and cannot move any further. Eventually, one has a branched, rather spidery-looking collection of queens.

Quite unexpectedly, massive computer simulations have shown that DLA clusters are fractal. They are nearly self-similar, that is, small portions are very much like reduced versions of large portions. But clusters deviate from randomised linear self-similarity, something that will pose interesting challenges for the future.

One reason for the importance of DLA is that it concerns the interface between the smooth and the fractal. Moving away again from randomness to deterministic chaos, and from physical to imaginary objects, let us

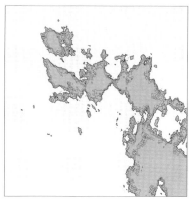

Figure 8 A fractal coastline that never was (B. B. Mandelbrot)

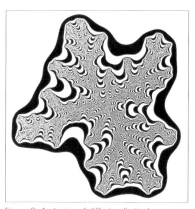

Figure 9 A cluster of diffusion limited aggregation, surrounded by its equipotential curves (C. J. G. Evertsz and B. B. Mandelbrot)

Figure 10 Quadratic Julia sets for the map $Z^2 + C$. Each boundary of a zebra stripe corresponds to a different value of C (B. B. Mandelbrot)

Figure 11 The Mandelbrot Set, surrounded by its equipotential curves

consider Julia sets. What will remain unchanged is that we shall deal with spiky sets surrounded by smooth lines.

An example of a "filled-in Julia set" is shown in Figure 10. This is generated by iteration of the simple function $Z^2 + C$. Under iteration the result of each evaluation provides the starting point to the next evaluation; because Z and C may be complex numbers, negative values can occur. For starting points outside the black shape, iteration will go to infinity; if you start inside, you fail to iterate to infinity. The boundary between black and white is called the Julia curve. It is approximately self-similar. Each chunk is not quite identical to a bigger chunk, because of non-linear deformation. But it is astonishing that iteration should create any form of self-similarity, quite spontaneously.

As in the investigation of fractal mountains, the computer was essential to the study of iteration. The bulk of fractal geometry is concerned with shapes of great apparent complication and by hand they could never be drawn. More precisely, this picture could have been computed by a hundred people working for years; but nobody would have started such an enormous calculation, without first feeling that it was worth performing.

Not only had I access to a computer in 1979, but I was familiar with its power. Therefore, I felt these calculations were worth trying, even though I certainly did not know what was going to come out. A fishing expedition led to a primitive form of Figure 11. The Julia sets of the

map $Z^2 + C$ can take all kinds of shapes, and a small change in C can change the Julia set very greatly. I set out to classify all the possible shapes and came up with a new shape, that has come to be known as the *Mandelbrot Set*, M. Figure 3 shows a tiny portion of Figure 11.

As you zoom towards a portion of the boundary of *M*, part of what you see is simply a repetition of something you have already seen. This element of repetition is essential to beauty. But beauty also requires an element of change and that is also very clearly present. As you come closer and closer, what you see becomes more and more complicated. The overall shape is the same, but the hair structure becomes more and more intense. This feature is *not* something we put in on purpose. Insofar as mathematics is not invented but discovered. It is something that has been there forever and it shows that the mathematics of $Z^2 + C$ is astonishingly complicated, by contrast with the simplicity of the formula. We find that the *M* set, when examined closer and closer and closer, exhibits the coexistence of the relentless repetition of the same theme combined with variety that boggles the imagination. I first saw the Mandelbrot Set on a black and white screen of very low graphic quality, and the picture looked dirty. But when we zoomed on what seemed like dirt we found instead an extraordinary little copy of the whole.

In Figure 11, the Mandelbrot Set is the *white* "bug" in the middle. It is very rough-edged, but is surrounded by a collection of zebra stripes whose edges become increasingly smooth as one goes away from *M*.

These zebra stripe edges happen to be Laplacian equipotential curves – just like in Figure 9. But they are far easier to obtain.

Of course, the black and white figures in this introduction are far from the beautiful colour ones which everyone must have seen. The structure itself is independent of the colour rendering. However, different renderings emphasise very different structural aspects. This use of colour is similar to that employed in relief maps, where altitude bands are signified by different colours. Perhaps surprisingly, the black and white of Bill Hirst's photographs serves to clarify their structural content.

Let me now bring together the separate strings of this introduction. How did fractals come to play their role of "extracting order out of chaos?" The key resides in the following very surprising discovery I made thanks to computer graphics.

The algorithms that generate fractals are typically so extraordinarily short, as to look positively dumb. This means they must be called "simple." Their fractal outputs, to the contrary, often appear to involve structures of great richness. A priori, one would have expected that the construction of complex shapes would necessitate complex rules.

What is the special feature that makes fractal geometry perform in such an unusual manner? The answer is very simple. The algorithms are recursive, and the computer code written to implement them involves "loops." That is, the basic instructions are simple, and their effects can be followed easily.

But let these simple instructions be performed repeatedly and – unless one deals with the simple old fractals, such as the Sierpinski gasket – the process of iteration effectively builds up an increasingly complicated transform, whose effects the mind can follow less and less easily. Eventually, one reaches something that is "qualitatively" different from the original building block. One can say that the situation is a fulfilment of what in general is nothing but a dream: the hope of describing and explaining "chaotic" nature as the cumulation of many simple steps.

Benoit Mandelbrot · Yorktown Heights · August 1994

Further reading

The Fractal Geometry of Nature by B B Mandelbrot, W H Freeman, 1982 was the first comprehensive book on the subject, and remains a basic reference book

The basic how-to book is *The Science of Fractal Images* (eds H-O Peitgen and D Saupe) (Springer 1988)

The best known book on iteration is *The Beauty of Fractals* by H-O Peitgen and P H Richter (Springer 1986)

For other aspects of the mathematics, *Fractals: Mathematical Foundations and Applications* by K J Falconer (J Wiley 1990)

On the concrete uses of fractals, two references are convenient, because they are special volumes of widely available periodicals

The first is *Proceedings of the Royal Society of London*, Volume A 423: (May 8 1989), which was also reprinted as *Fractals in the Natural Sciences* eds M Fleischmann et al. (Princeton University Press 1990)

The second is *Physica D*, Volume 38, which was also reprinted as *Fractals in Physics, Essays in Honor of B B Mandelbrot on his 65th birthday* (eds A Aharony and J Feder) (North Holland 1989)

On the physics, a standard textbook is *Fractals* by J Feder (Plenum 1988)

On some philosophical or social issues, see the *Survol* appended to the 3rd edition of my book, *Les objets fractals* (Flammarion 1989)

Many of my original papers will be reprinted in a multivolume series of *Selecta*; unfortunately, my wish to do them right keeps postponing the publication

Plates

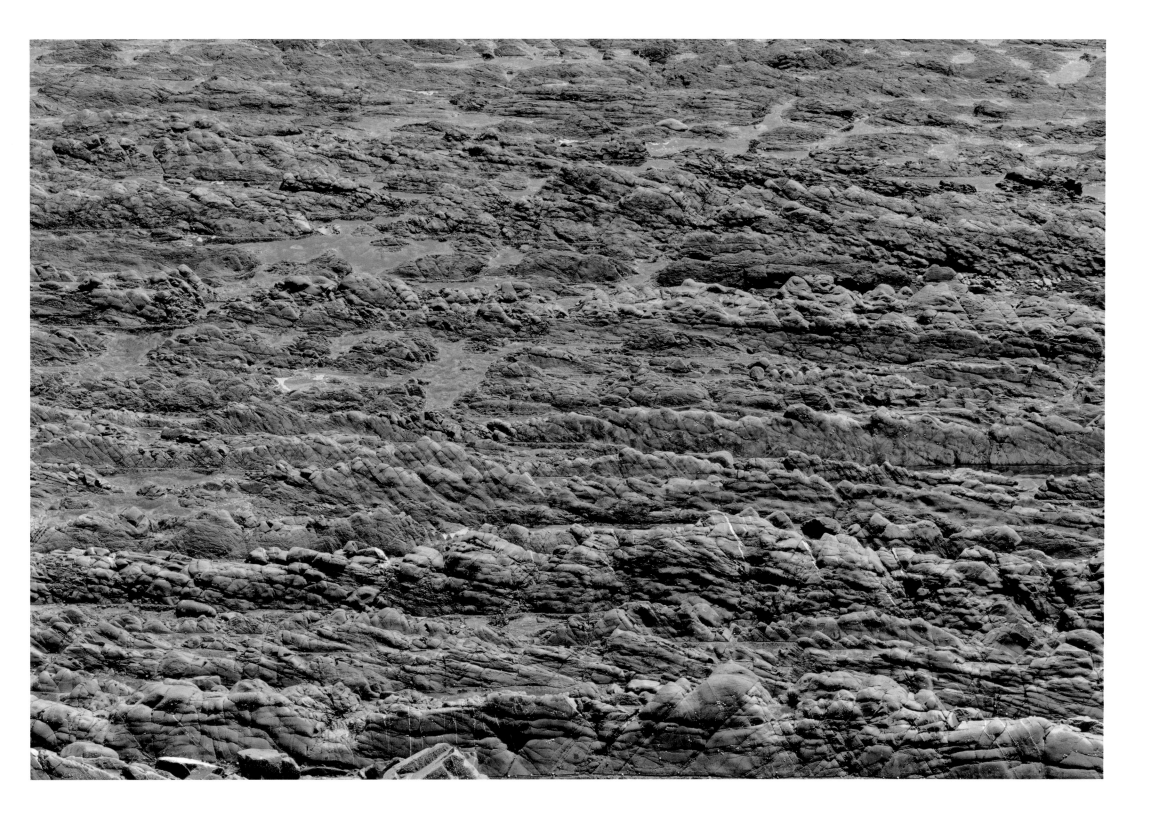

Captions

The slopes of Beinn Dorain, Strathclyde, Scotland. The foreground markings are drainage ditches cut before planting with conifers. The main Glasgow railway line can just be seen at the foot of the mountain. 1991

Sloping limestone pavement at Hutton Roof Crags, Cumbria, England. The limestone is slowly dissolved by water and as the lower rivulets of each slab remain wet longer, they are more deeply eroded. The effect becomes amplified because the deep rivulets are sheltered from the drying effect of the wind. 1991

Near Llyn Brianne in the Cambrian Mountains, Wales. Vast areas of this region are covered in tussock grass. The patterning on the steepest part of the hillside is soil creep. 1991

The Black Ven, near Lyme Regis, England; this is Europe's largest active landslip. The periodic slumping of the hill is due to impermeable clay strata overlain with sands, which become unstable when saturated with water. This is a rare example in Britain of a completely natural landscape. 1991

Left: The Blue Mesa, Petrified Forest, Arizona. These soft mudstone formations erode rapidly under the effect of sudden rainstorms to produce "badlands": so named by the pioneers because of the difficulty in crossing them. The immediate foreground is about 2 metres across. 1988

Right: Looking down from Pen-y-Fan in the Brecon Beacons, Wales. This complex of tributaries combine to form Nant Cynwyn; the white dots in the picture are sheep. The scene is several hundred metres across. 1991

Olive groves near Alhondiga, province of Guadalajara, Spain. The originally straight lines of the olive trees have become distorted by soil slipping down the steep hillsides. Less productive groves have been abandoned; trees have died and natural ground cover has begun to return. 1986

Stone-wall field system near Robledo de Chavela, province of Madrid, Spain. The land here has been divided and subdivided through inheritance – until the smaller fields became unviable and were left to go wild. 1989

Water spillway, alongside the Roosevelt Dam, Arizona, USA. This man-made irregular concrete structure dissipates the potentially damaging energy of water cascading down from the sluice gates. An irregular design, with a balance of small- and large-scale features, is the most effective way of doing this. 1988

Telford in Shropshire, England. The industrial revolution started in this area because of the local availability of several key mineral deposits. This road cutting is decorated – using locally produced tiles – with a simplified representation of the region's geology: the reason for the town's existence. 1991

Sea defences at Colwyn Bay, Wa These concrete shapes, called Do units, dissipate wave energy by crea turbulence: slowing down the wa gradually. This prevents beach mate being stripped away and promotes be growth. Randomly placed, the u become highly interlocked, preven movement and damage. Mr Dolos the idea after trying to salvage a ca of anchors from a sunken ship! 199

Arches National Park in Utah, USA. A desert region where lack of nutrient and limited moisture lead to a remarkably even plant distribution. The extensive root systems of larger plants reduce the water available to close neighbours. Creosote plants go one step further by releasing toxins into the surrounding soil. 1988

Tidal estuary at Laconnell, Donegal, Eire. This muddy estuary is pock-marked by worm casts and seaweeds. 1991

The Mawddach estuary, North Wales. An extremely low tide reveals the highly complex meandering channels of this extensive, well developed, sandy estuary. 1991

Eggborough Power Station and fuel ash settling ponds, Yorkshire, England. The ash from the power station furnaces is mixed with water and pumped to ponds, where the ash is deposited and valuable by-products are skimmed off for sale. When the mound of ash becomes too high for efficient pumping, it is grassed over and planted irregularly with trees in an attempt to disguise it as natural. 1991

Petrified Forest National Park, Arizona, USA. The petrified tree trunks start intact, but snap into progressively shorter sections – like vertebrae – as the supporting sands shift. These sections then gradually move apart as they continue to erode down to sand. 1988

Giant's Causeway, Co. Antrim, Northern Ireland. These basalt columns a natural feature formed from lava. the skin of the lava cools, it shrinks, ating a polygonal pattern: similar to seen in dried mud. The pattern pagates into the hotter lava as a result he preferential local cooling that the cks promote. 1991

Basalt columns near Fingal's cave on the Isle of Staffa, The Hebrides, Scotland. The polygonal columns grow perpendicular to the cooling surface of the lava. A convoluted structure, such as this, suggests some movement or change in thermal conditions during the cooling process. The structure is reminiscent of a breaking wave: reflecting the fluid nature of the lava from which it formed. 1991

Grouse moor near Leadhills, Scotland: patterned by periodic strip burning. Grouse need a mixture of young heather to feed on and adjoining mature growth for cover and nesting; but heather more than 15 years old is impenetrable. The land manager tries to maximise the number of breeding pairs per acre by providing the optimum balance and distribution of growth. 1991

Dungeon Hill, Dumfries and Galloway, Scotland. A highly fractured granite outcrop. 1991

Vertical rock strata seen from a cliff top near Hartland Quay, Devon, England. These strata lie in the inter-tidal zone; note the limpet clusters. 1991

Blaenau Ffestiniog, North Wales. A mountain of slate offcuts, discarded from the slate quarries above. The large outcrops at the head of the precarious tip are built to help stabilise it. The chapel to the left is the artist David Nash's studio. 1991

Chester, England, M53 motorway bridge construction site. These workers are wiring together steel reinforcement bars for the bridge's foundations. 1990

Looking across from Barmouth to Fegla Fach, North Wales. Patterned sandbanks at the mouth of the Mawddach estuary seen at low tide. The marks that look like lizard tracks were made by canoeists dragging their boats to the water. 1991

Maghera Strand, Co Donegal, Eire. This extensive sandy estuary is patterned by the combined effects of wind and sea. These tend to sort the sand, grouping together grains of similar size and density. Where the beach is a mixture of sands derived from different coloured rocks, this can result in patterning. 1991

Petrified Forest, Arizona, USA. These dried-up river beds contrast with the black stones covering the surrounding land. The stones have a thin, black coating called "desert varnish". Minerals from within the rock migrate to the surface, drawn out by moisture, and oxidise to form a dark patina. 1988

Detail from Petrified Forest, Arizona, USA. Desert varnish takes several thousand years to develop fully. Lighter areas show where the ground has been disturbed or where other materials have become concentrated, such as silt in the river beds. Where a rock splits the revealed face can appear white in comparison to the older surfaces. 1988

Maiden Castle ancient hill fort, Dorset, England. These natural-looking hills were con-structed by hand, starting around 350BC. The unnatural-looking lines are natural: caused by soil creep on the steep slopes, stabilised by the effect of sheep "contouring" as they graze. The entrance to the fort was built in a maze-like pattern to confuse attacking forces. It didn't work against the Romans: who captured it in 43AD! 1991

Near Womersley, North Yorkshi England; colliery waste being spre out and compacted by giant ea movers. 1991

Upper picture: a turbulent and foamy sea produced by the combined effects of a strong wind and a fast tide driving waves in over an extended rocky foreshore; North Devon, England. 1991

Lower picture: Rocky limestone foreshore at Doolin on the edge of the Burren, Co Clare, Eire. 1991

Canyonlands in Utah, USA. Rock strata interspersed with sandier deposits give rise to a distinctive layered structure. The light-coloured meandering line is a dried-up river bed. 1988

View down from Mount Snowdon, North Wales. Despite the abundance of water, this highly exposed site constitutes marginal conditions for the vegetation: hence the patterning reminiscent of some of the desert pictures. 1989

Near Tyndrum, Central Region, Scotland. Extensive snow patches remain on these mountains late into the spring. 1991

Lightning strike, Petrified Forest, Arizona, USA. Similarities between the shapes of lightning and rivers are not coincidental. Lightning takes the path of least resistance through an electrical potential; a river takes the path of least resistance through a gravitational potential. Both potentials have the same mathematical form: a $1/r$ dependence. 1988

Unusual rock strata near Speke's Mill Mouth, North Devon, England. 1991

Left: The "Organ Pipes", basalt columns at the entrance to Fingal's Cave, Isle of Staffa, The Hebrides, Scotland. Large regular columns such as these form when lava cools very slowly. This occurs deep down, where the thermal conditions are most stable. 1991

Right: These basalt columns are part of the Giant's Causeway, Co Antrim, Northern Ireland. Contrary to popular belief, the basalt features of Staffa and the Giant's Causeway are not linked beneath the sea. 1991

Bryce Canyon, Utah, USA. These rock spires are called "hoodoos". They result from impermeable rocks protecting softer – soluble – rocks beneath from the erosional effect of rain. Careful inspection of the photograph will reveal the surprisingly large scale of the phenomenon – look for the pine trees! 1988

Tonto National Forest, Arizona, USA. The striking parallelism of these cacti contrasts with their chaotic distribution on the hillside, and that of the other plants. This is a near-perfect visual analogue to the structure of a liquid-crystal or magnet. 1988

Bill Hirst   AFTERWORD

KISS is an abbreviation familiar to generations of soldiers; it stands for "Keep It Simple Stupid". It serves as reminder that reliability is born of simplicity, and for those whose lives are at stake – reliability is at a premium. Scientists too are exhorted to prefer the simple to the complicated: the scientific method is underpinned by a principle known as "Occam's Razor". This holds that the simplest adequate explanation should always be preferred to unnecessarily more complicated alternatives.

At first sight, a preference for simplicity over complexity seems no more than "common sense". Complicated tasks in all walks of life are routinely broken down into manageable stages or steps, which are tackled individually before reassembly into some overall solution or result. This approach – an intellectual "divide and rule" – is called reductionism; it has been a major factor in the successful development of science and technology over the centuries.

Despite its impressive record though, reductionism suffers from some fundamental limitations. Perhaps most seriously, it cannot cope with phenomena involving the mutual or even self-interaction of a system's constituent parts. Examples of such systems or processes would be weather forecasting, evolution, ecology, embryology, economics, epidemiology, fluid dynamics, traffic flow and so on.

For each of these "the whole is greater than the sum of the parts": a crowd is qualitatively different from the individuals that comprise it. When an element of feed-back is present, cause and effect are no longer proportionate, they become non-linear.

As an example of non-linear behaviour, consider a simple light-switch; a relatively large force brings the switch to a point where a minute additional force produces a dramatically greater result: the switch moves from off to on. In non-linear systems, the chain of cause and effect, fundamental to reductionism, becomes hopelessly tangled, cross-linked and branched. Which force switched the light on – was it the large force or the minute additional one?

Non-linear problems can't be solved by the neat and tidy methods of traditional mathematics; they require what amounts to a glorified trial-and-error approach – and most of the problems are insoluble anyway! It's hardly surprising then that scientists and mathematicians throughout the history of science have concentrated on dealing with linear systems and linear problems; after all, scientists were educated and examined using exclusively linear examples. If non-linear characteristics appeared, the problem would be modified by simplification, approximation or idealisation – whatever was necessary to make it soluble. Unfortunately, while slight approximations in a linear problem produce only slight inaccuracies in the answer, this is not so for non-linear problems. The simplification or approximation that makes a non-linear problem tractable is frequently tantamount to "throwing out the baby with the bathwater".

The fruit of this "love affair with linearity" was science's capacity to describe what was happening 15 billion years ago during the first microsecond of the big bang; but science's failure was its inability to describe a vegetable! Just what was it about Cauliflower Romanesco that made it so appealing? It may not seem as grand an enquiry, but even an untutored eye can see that Cauliflower Romanesco – and numerous other plants – share some fundamental structural affinity. Thanks to Mandelbrot, we now recognise that property as self-similarity. He provided a language with which to discuss, and a geometry with which to quantify, these properties.

Even before the arrival of the new language of fractal geometry, recognising structural similarities was already well established – if uncoordinated. The most widely known example being D'Arcy Thompson's remarkable book *On Growth and Form*. What such intuitive approaches lacked was any insight into the reasons for such structural similarities. There was an intuition (correct) of a connection, without any methodology for substantiating that connection or explaining how it had arisen.

The arrival of fractal geometry meant that what might have been considered a vaguely metaphysical pursuit – identifying similarities, say, between the veins of a leaf and the river system on whose bank it grew – became more than an argument by analogy; it became quantifiable, capable of prediction – testable and hence truly scientific. Fractal geometry provided answers to questions that had previously been unanswerable – if they could be formulated at all; it returned

science to dealing with the real and everyday world: a world of mountains, rivers, clouds and trees.

But *how* do the shapes of fractal geometry come to appear in the world beyond the computer screen? The answer lies in the process by which they are generated. Fractals arise from iterative processes: where the outcome of an operation provides the input for its repetition. This obviously makes them well-suited to computer generation. However, much of what shapes us and our environment is also iterative: evolution, growth and erosion being prime examples. Each generation, each cell division and each flash-flood, makes an incremental change which in turn provides the starting point for the next cycle. It is the shared, formative role of iteration that produces the similarities between computer-generated fractals and those of natural structures.

What's more, this is a process whose influence extends beyond the structures of the physical world to include the intangible constructs of civilisation: the distribution of city population sizes, price fluctuations, income distributions ... Even that most special human attribute, language, displays a fractal signature in the distribution of word frequency versus word ranking. This relationship holds from the most frequently used word down to the 10,000th most frequently used word – and it holds for several languages. If language structure reflects our mental processes, then it seems that even our thought patterns must be fractal.

Fractal patterns possess the maximum complexity for the information they contain; the instructions to produce the shape of a tree could be summarised as "grow, bifurcate, repeat". Imagine how much information would be required for a numerically controlled milling machine to produce a convincing tree shape! The information efficiency with which fractal forms can be described makes them ideal for transmission, whether it's from one generation to another via a small seed – or from one computer to another via a fractally compressed data file. It also means that fractal shapes are the signature of order emerging from chaos, of information buried in noise.

In the eye/brain, evolution has provided us with the ultimate pattern recognition tool; our ability to recognise, distinguish and exploit pattern has been central to our survival as a species. We delight in pattern recognition, for what else is music, poetry, drama … in short – Art – other than communication of the otherwise ineffable. But it is not the arid patterning of conventional geometry or rigid symmetries the eye/brain seeks; how long does one look at a scene reflected in water? – Only long enough to confirm that it is an imperfect reflection, and hence genuine. Contrast the experience of examining a hand-knotted oriental rug with that of seeing a machine-made copy; the pleasure in the first comes from its slight irregularities, the breaking of pattern within a greater pattern – the deliberate error; the machine-made version is regular and perfect: *perfectly* boring.

When I began taking the pictures that evolved into this project, I set out on a simple technical exercise. The idea was to take highly detailed photographs of large areas of the ground – a sort of large-scale version of what the Boyle Family had done with their fibre-glass casts of randomly selected points of the Earth's surface. The early photographs had much of the appeal of anonymous aerial reconnaissance photographs or satellite images – a bewilderingly complex interweaving of pure, objective information. Examining them, I noticed how even the most complex scenes contained subtle, larger-scale structure, which transcended the individual details. What's more, similarities emerged between completely different types of landscape, sometimes thousands of miles apart. This was not the photographically very familiar territory of man-imposed order versus nature's untamed disorder – quite the opposite: it seemed to concern the emergence of spontaneous natural order.

The photograph of the Roosevelt Dam spillway played an important role in the project's development. In this picture, the man-made irregularity (constructed for a functional purpose) and the adjoining shattered rock underlined that the visual interest derived from the shared element of chaotic behaviour (using "chaotic" in its newer scientific sense of aperiodic order rather than mere randomness). For a brief time I changed my working title for the project from "Groundworks" to "Natural Order and Chaos by Design" and sought out examples of other functionally irregular man-made structures: camouflage, climbing walls, grouse moor, breakwaters, concert halls with acoustic panels based on prime number series, and so on …

Gathering the pictures together, I was struck by how similar many of them appeared. People looking at them would continually mistake the natural for the man-made and vice versa; frequently they would think the scene was much larger or smaller than it was, or become disorientated. Finally, I realised that both categories were really the same: they each presented the graphical face of chaos – they were fractal.

Despite my keeping to the original – simple – goal of just photographing the ground, the results had become complex. They exhibited the classic characteristic of a fractal: a symmetry of scale between the large and the small, a consistency that was without repetition. The iterative nature of the project, in which each stage modified the next, and the cooperative effect of combining pictures, produced not just fractal photographs – but a project whose own winding path echoed those in the photographs.

Bill Hirst · Chester · August 1994

ACKNOWLEDGEMENTS

Many people have helped me to complete this project and produce the book and touring exhibition that support it. I am particularly indebted to Steve Makin and Paul Hill for contributing their insight, advice and criticism. Above all though, I would like to thank my wife Alison for accompanying me on the early travel for this project, and coping with the disruption to family life the latter stages involved.

Others have helped by providing access, information, suggestions of sites, accommodation, transport, advice, encouragement, criticism, and the opportunity to disseminate the work.

My thanks to them all:

Alison Buchan, Andrew Dixon, Barry Lane, Berris Connoly, Bill Bishop, Brett Rogers, Brian Arneil, Charlie Meecham, Chester Arts Services, Chris Bullock, Chris Townsend, Christine Rawnsley, Dave Rodgers, Dave Williams, David Falconer, Dewi Lewis, Don Burnet, Eddie Ephraums, Fay Godwin, Fiona Porteous, Gill Rosson, Gill Scott, Gordon Stent, Harold Walmsley, Hiroaki Kubota, Ian Hamilton Finlay, Ian Hughes, Ian Robertson, Juan Alberto Gaviria, Jill Staples, Johnathan LeVay, John Davies, John Scrivener, John Tolchard, John Tweed, Kerry Byrne, Martina Mettner, Mathew Neal, Mark Haworth-Booth, Martha McCulloch, Michael Collins, National Power, Neil Wilkie, Niall Allsop, North West Arts Board, Paul Bardwell, Paul Taylor, Peter Boulding, Peter Burgis, Peter Cattrell, Peter Haggarty, Peter Tromans, Ray Johnson, Ray Thorp, Richard Selfe, Richard Tailby, Roger Taylor, Salford Cultural Services, Scottish Nature Conservancy Council, Severn Trent Water, Sheffield Arts Department, Shell Research Ltd, Sid Barlow, Shona Falconer, Stephen Snoddy, Steve Brake, Steve and Janet Skippon, Sue Benson, The British Council, The Centro Colombo Americano, The Photographers' Place, Tim Edwards, Tim Elkerton, Tom Andrews, Tracy Colgan, Trevor Parkinson, Virginia Tandy, Welsh Water, Wendy Hughes, William Hardie, Yorkshire & Humberside Arts

An exhibition of these photographs will tour the UK from 1994 to 1996; for further information please contact:

Untitled Gallery, 1 Brown Street, Sheffield S1 2BS
Tel 0114 272 5947

Original prints of the photographs in this book are available for purchase from:

The Zelda Cheatle Gallery, 8 Cecil Court, London WC2N 4HE
Tel 0171 836 0506 Fax 0171 497 8911

In Autumn 1995 the exhibition will tour to venues in South America with the support of the British Council and the Centro Colombo Americano, Medellin, Colombia.

The exhibition will also be exhibited in the United States of America: interested curators should write to Bill Hirst.

I will be continuing work on this project, and wish to include sites throughout the world. I would welcome opportunities to visit and photograph in other countries. I would also welcome suggestions of sites to photograph that display the characteristics shown in this book. I will provide a free 20" x 24" print to anyone suggesting a new site that I am able to use in my next book. Suggestions should include a picture of the site (that I may keep) and be accompanied by a map showing its exact location.

Correspondence should be addressed to:

Bill Hirst, 27 Hamilton Street, Chester CH2 3JG England
E-mail: hirst@trc.sirm.nl

The design of this book was developed with financial assistance from North West Arts Board.

Left The Old Gang lead mine in Swaledale, North Yorkshire   *Above* The Present Order, 1983, by Ian Hamilton Finlay with Nicholas Sloan